THE SECOND
PHILLIP SCHOFIELD
FUN FILE

Also available:

The Phillip Schofield Fun File

The Second Phillip Schofield Fun File

Illustrated by
TONY BLUNDELL

BANTAM BOOKS
TORONTO · NEW YORK · LONDON · SYDNEY · AUCKLAND

THE SECOND PHILLIP SCHOFIELD FUN
FILE

A BANTAM BOOK 0 553 175505

First publication in Great Britain

PRINTING HISTORY
Bantam Edition published 1989

This book is set in 11/12 pt Garamond
by Colset Private Limited, Singapore.

Bantam Books are published by Transworld Publishers Ltd.,
61–63 Uxbridge Road, Ealing, London W5 5SA, in Australia
by Transworld Publishers (Australia) Pty. Ltd., 15–23 Helles
Avenue, Moorebank, NSW 2170, and in New Zealand by
Transworld Publishers (N.Z.) Ltd., Cnr. Moselle and
Waipareira Avenues, Henderson, Auckland.

Made and printed in Great Britain by
Cox & Wyman Ltd., Reading, Berks.

Contents

Introduction

So many of you out there enjoyed my first Fun File that those nice people at Bantam Books have asked me to do another one — and here it is!

I promise you that the jokes in this second book will have you groaning even louder than the first ones, the puzzles will keep you guessing even longer than before, and the brain-teasers will have you pulling out what little of your hair you have left!

And there's not a gopher in sight . . .

Have fun!

HYSTERICAL HOWLERS

Why did the chicken cross the road?
  To see Gregory Peck!

Did you hear about the chimpanzees who escaped from the zoo? They used a monkey wrench to get out. . .

Doctor to Patient: Which do you want first – the good news or the bad news?
  Patient: The bad news first.
Doctor: The bad news is that we've amputated the wrong leg.
  Patient: So what's the good news?
Doctor: The patient in the next bed wants to buy your slippers.

Why couldn't the lemon finish her phone conversation with the orange?
  Because the pips went. . .

Which letter can't you find in the alphabet?
  The one in the post.

What sits on a lily pad and says 'Cloak, cloak'?
  A Chinese frog. . .

What happens to refrigerators when they die?
  They lose their cool. . .

Teacher to Pupil: I thought I told you never to be late for school again.

    Pupil: But I did set the alarm clock for eight, Miss.
Teacher: So why are you late?
    Pupil: There's nine of us at home, Miss.

One of the BBC's producers went into the newsagent's shop the other day. In one ear she had some jelly and in the other a lot of blancmange. She bought her newspaper.

    'That'll be 35p, please,' said the shop assistant.

    'Pardon?'

    'That'll be 35p, please,' repeated the shop assistant.

    'You'll have to speak up,' she said. 'I'm afraid I'm a trifle deaf.'

How do you say hello to a drunken Italian?

    'Hi, *tiddly Iti. . .*'

What's grey and has four legs and a trunk?
   A mouse going on holiday.

What's brown and has four legs and a trunk?
   A mouse coming back off holiday.

What's black and white and laughs?
   The nun who pushed the other nun down the hill.

Two tomatoes, Fred and Bert, strolled into the Wild West Saloon. Which one of them was the cowboy?
   Neither – they were both redskins.

What happened to the burglar who stole a calendar?
He got twelve months.

What did the judge say to his dentist?
'Do you promise to pull the tooth, the whole tooth and nothing but the tooth?'

What's black and white, black and white, black and white?
A nun rolling down a hill. . .

During a revolution in a foreign country a famous spy was captured by the rebels. He was tied up and led in front of a firing squad. The rebels' leader came up to him and asked him if he had any special requests.

How do you make anti-freeze?
  Stick her in the fridge.

  'Yes,' said the spy. 'Before I die I'd like to sing my favourite song.'
  'Very well. What is it?'
  'Twenty-nine million green bottles standing on the wall. . . .'

And why did the turkey not cross the road?
  To prove that he wasn't a chicken.

Parent to son: What did your teacher say when he saw your homework?

    Son: Shall I leave out the bad language?

Parent: Yes.

    Son: Not a word.

What do you call an Irishman who's been dead for three thousand years?

    Peat.

Why did the dinosaur cross the road?

    Because chickens hadn't been invented then.

What do you give to the man who has everything?

    Penicillin.

A man walks into a pub with a parrot on his shoulder. 'You can't come in here with a pig, sir,' said the barman.

'Don't be silly, this isn't a pig,' said the man.

'I was talking to the parrot. . .'

Teacher: What is frozen water?
  Pupil: Iced water.
Teacher: What is frozen cream?
  Pupil: Ice cream.
Teacher: And what is frozen ink?
  Pupil: Iced ink.
Teacher: Yes I know. Why don't you go home and have a bath?

What's green and turns red at the touch of a button?
  A frog in a liquidiser.

Knock, knock.
  Who's there?
Shirley.
  Shirley Who?
Shirley you were expecting me?

Knock, knock.
  Who's there?
Harry.
  Harry Who?
Harry up and let me in!

Knock, knock.
  Who's there?
Little old lady.
  Little old lady Who?
I didn't know you could yodel!

Knock, knock.
  Who's there?
Luke.
  Luke Who.
Luke through the window and see.

Knock, knock.
  Who's there?
Granny.
  Granny Who?
Knock, knock.
  Who's there?
Granny.
  Granny Who?

Knock, knock.
  Who's there?
Granny.
  Granny Who?

Knock, knock.
  Who's there?
Auntie.
  Auntie Who?
Auntie glad you got rid of all those grannies?

Knock, knock.
  Who's there?
Amanda.
  Amanda Who?
Amanda fix the washing machine.

Knock, knock.
  Who's there?
Doris.
  Doris Who?
Doris locked and that's why I'm knocking.

Knock, knock.
  Who's there?
Alec.
  Alec Who?
A electric fire keeps you warm in the winter.

Knock, knock.
  Who's there?
Evelyn.
  Evelyn Who?
Evelyn All!

Knock, knock.
  Who's there?
Janet.
  Janet Who?
Janet your own sweaters?

Knock, knock.
  Who's there?
Len.
  Len Who?
Lend me a fiver, will you?

Knock, knock.
  Who's there?
Connie.
  Connie Who?
Connie not come and open the door?

Knock, knock.
  Who's there?
Alice.
  Alice Who?
I listened carefully but I couldn't hear anything.

Knock, knock.
  Who's there?
Annie.
  Annie Who?
Anniebody here know where Matthew is?

Knock, knock.
  Who's there?
Matthew(*so that's where he was!*).
  Matthew Who?
Matthew always talk with a lisp?

Knock, knock.
  Who's there?
Ivor.
  Ivor Who?
Ivor one don't find Knock Knock jokes very funny.

Knock, knock.
Who's there?
Fraser.
Fraser Who?
Fraser jolly good fellow.

One night a policeman approached an unsavoury looking character on the street corner. 'I'm afraid I'm going to have to ask you to accompany me to the police station, sir,' he said.

'Whatever for?'

'Well, it's dark and I'm scared to go there on my own.'

How many yuppies does it take to change a lightbulb?
Two – one to find the Filofax and one to phone the electrician.

How many Sloane Rangers does it take to change a lightbulb?
Ten – one to change the bulb and nine to discuss whether it's socially acceptable.

How many Californians does it take to change a lightbulb?
Forty – one to change the bulb and thirty-nine to share the experience.

A hearse was climbing up a very steep hill when the coffin in the back fell out and slid down the hill. It slid all the way down the High Street, until it finally crashed to a halt outside the local chemist's. Which only goes to prove that you should always go to a chemist to stop your coffin. . .

How many punks does it take to change a lightbulb?
Two - one to change the bulb and one to knock the chair away.

Three tomatoes – Father, Mother and Son Tomato – were on their way to the supermarket. Father and Mother were going ahead at a great pace but Son Tomato was lagging behind a little. Impatiently, Father Tomato looked over his shoulder and shouted: 'Come on, Son, ketchup!'

Teacher: Give me a sentence which includes the word 'judicious'.
   Pupil: Hands that judicious can be soft as your face. . .

Teacher: What's the definition of the word 'minimum'?
   Pupil: A very short mother?

What do you call a man who wears a raincoat?
   Mac.

And what do you call a man who wears two raincoats?
   Max.

What should you prescribe for a sick pig?
Oinkment.

How can you throw a boomerang and make sure that it doesn't come back to you?
Throw it down a one-way street.

A Texan millionaire was being shown around Australia by a friend. When the friend showed him Ayers Rock, he said, 'Why, it sure is pretty, but back home in Texas we've got pebbles that are as big as that.'

Next he showed him the Sydney Opera House. 'That's very nice,' said the Texan, 'but back home in Texas we've got cottages as big as that.'

Finally the friend, who was now understandably feeling a little irritated, took the Texan into the Bush, where a kangaroo bounded past them.

'Whatever was that?' asked the Texan.

'A grasshopper,' said the Australian. . .

Why was the cobra so upset?
Because he'd just bit his tongue.

We all know that one hedgehog crossed the road to join his flatmates, but why did the other hedgehog cross the road?
To show that he had guts. . .

Mother Cannibal to Son: How many times must I tell you not to eat your chips with your fingers? Put your fingers on a side plate and eat them later.

What do you call a row of men all waiting to get a haircut?
A barbeque.

We all know what you get if you pour boiling water down a rabbit hole but what do you get when you burn your mother's cakes?

A hot cross mum.

Girl to Boy: Our love is like a ship on the ocean.
Boy: You mean beautiful and romantic?
Girl: No, wet and wooden.

How do you make a banana split?

Chop it in half.

What is purple and screams?

A damson in distress.

Gordon went into the local sweetshop to buy some chocolate. As soon as he asked for them the shopkeeper and his wife dashed past him, out of the shop and into the street.

'What's wrong?' asked Gordon. 'I only asked for some chocolate.'

'Yes, I know,' said the shopkeeper. 'But we've run out.'

How do you make a bandstand?
Take all the chairs away.

What's the definition of illegal?
A very sick bird.

What do Winnie the Pooh and William the Conqueror have in common?

Their middle name.

Passenger to Bus Inspector: How long will the next bus be?

Inspector: Oh, about fifteen feet, madam.

What did Cinderella say when the chemist lost her photographs?

'Someday my prints will come.'

Why doesn't Dracula get married?

Because he wants to remain a batchelor.

What do you call a farmer who used to like tractors, but doesn't anymore?

An ex-tractor fan.

What do you call a deer with no eyes?

No-eye deer.

And what do you call a deer with no eyes and no legs?

Still no-eye deer.

What's the fastest cake in the world?

It's scone.

What do you call a mushroom in McDonalds who buys Cokes and Big Macs for everyone?
 A fun guy (fungi) to be with. . .

What do you call a sheep in a sauna?
 A woolly sweater.

What do elephants have that no other animals have?
 Baby elephants. . . .

Why do elephants hate penguins?
 Because they can't get the wrappers off.

What's big and grey and has six legs?
An elephant – I lied about the legs.

Which has more legs – an elephant or no elephant?
No elephant because an elephant has four legs while no elephant has eight legs.

How does an elephant get down from a tree?
He sits on a leaf and waits until the autumn.

What's big and grey and never needs ironing?
A drip-dry elephant.

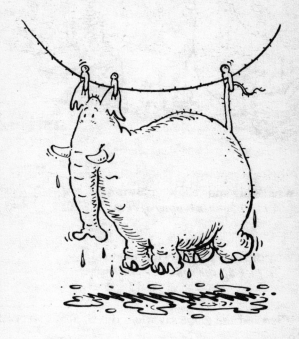

What's big and grey and wears glass slippers?
Cinderelephant.

What goes in grey and comes out blue?
An elephant swimming on a cold day.

What's big and yellow and swims?
An elephant in a bowl of custard.

Why did the elephant cross the road?
To pick up the squashed chicken. . .

What did the grape say when the elephant stepped on it?
Nothing at all – it just gave a little wine.

What do you call the elephants which are to be found at the South Pole?
Lost.

What do you get if you cross an elephant with a boy scout?
  An elephant that helps little old ladies across the road.

Where do elves go to do their shopping?
  To British Gnome Stores.

Waiter, waiter, there's a frog in my soup.
  I'm sorry, sir, but the fly's on holiday.

What should you give a deaf fisherman?
  A herring-aid.

How can you join the Navy?
  Handcuff two sailors together.

What is yellow and goes at 100 miles an hour?
An E-type banana.

Teacher: What's a polygon.
Pupil: A dead parrot?

What is made of metal, stands in the middle of Paris and wobbles?
The Trifle Tower.

Which country has the most energetic people?
Russia – the people are always Russian here and Russian there.

And which country has the slimmest people in the world?
Finland.

And what's the slimmest building in the world?
The Tower in Pisa – everyone sees it lean.

Mother to Pet Shop Owner: Can I have a dog for my little girl?
Pet Shop Owner: I'm sorry, madam, we don't do swaps.

What's a frog's favourite drink?
Croaka-Cola.

What do you call someone with a paper bag on his head?
Russell.

What is red, has wheels and lies on its back?
A dead bus.

How do you stop a bull from charging?
Take away all his credit cards.

Where are hippies to be found?
At the top of your leggies.

What do you call two burglars?
A pair of nickers.

Why are the skies of New York cleaner than London's?
Because of all the skyscrapers.

Waiter, waiter, there's a bee in my soup.
Well, it is alphabet soup, sir.

What's long and yellow and looks like a banana?
A banana.

Waiter, waiter, there's a dead newt in my wine.
Well, you did ask for something with a little body in it, sir.

Where do Martians go to drink?
To a Mars Bar.

What did the big strawberry say to the little strawberry?
If it wasn't for you I wouldn't be in this jam.

What's yellow and brown and travels at 110 miles per hour?
A train driver's sandwich.

Where do sheep go to get their hair cut?
The baa-baa's shop.

Why did the elephant sit on the orange?
Because he wanted to play squash.

Voice on telephone: I'm sorry Alistair can't come to school today.
Teacher: And to whom am I speaking?
Voice: This is my father. . .

How do you stop a skunk from smelling?
  Chop its nose off.

Why do you never see an elephant on a bicycle?
  Because they haven't got a thumb to ring the bell with.

How do you make a fruit punch?
  Start an argument between an apple and an orange.

What's yellow and leaps from cake to cake?
  Tarzipan.

Did you hear about the cannibal wedding where the bride and groom were toasted?

What do you get if you cross the Titanic with the Atlantic Ocean?

About half-way across. . .

'One of my ancestors died at Waterloo.'
  'Fighting against Napoleon?'
'No, he fell under a train.'

'Do you know how to keep an idiot in suspense?'
  'No.'
'OK, I'll tell you next week.'

What's the definition of a myth?

Thomeone who itn't a mithith. . .

What did the elephant say when the crocodile bit him on his trunk?

'I thuppothe you think thad's fuddy. . .'

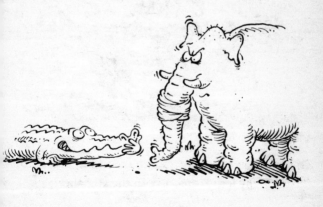

What do you call a three-humped camel?
Humphrey...

Where should you go to when you lose your vegetables?
The Missing Parsons Bureau.

Which birds live underground?
Mynah birds.

How many letters are there in the alphabet?
Twenty-four – ET went home.

What's the definition of a slug?
A snail with a housing problem.

Which two letters of the alphabet are particularly bad for your teeth?
D and K.

Teacher to Pupil: Recite the alphabet to me, please.
  Pupil: A,B,C,D,E,F,G,H,I,J,K,L,M,N,O,Q,R,S,T,U,V,W,X,Y,Z.
Teacher: That's very good, but where's the P?
  Pupil: Running down my leg, Miss. . .

Teacher to Pupil: Why did you miss school yesterday?
  Pupil: My aim wasn't very good, sir. . .

'Your daughter is a little spoilt.'
    'Nonsense! She's not spoilt at all!'
'You haven't seen what happened when the elephant fell on top of her. . .'

What did the rug say to the floor?
    'Don't move – I've got you covered!'

What did the toothpaste say to the toothbrush?
    'Give me a little squeeze and I'll meet you outside the tube.'

Why is Cinderella not a very good football player?
    Because she always keeps running away from the ball.

'I call my dog Isiah.'
  'Why's that?'
'Because one eye's higher than the other.'

'I call my dog Camera.'
  'Why's that?'
'Because he's always snapping. . .'

QUIRKY QUIZZES

MATCH TO MATCH

1. How good is your sports knowledge? See if you can match the following list of sports with the person most famous for playing that sport.

Sports	Sportsmen
1. Decathlon	Steve Davis
2. Running	Imran Khan
3. Skiing	Fatima Whitbread
4. Ice-skating	Gary Lineker
5. Cricket	Daley Thompson
6. Boxing	Duncan Goodhew
7. Javelin	Mike Tyson
8. Football	Jayne Torville
9. Snooker	Zola Budd
10. Swimming	Eddie Edwards

2. You might not find the following locations on any street map, but they are all places in popular television programmes. Can you tell which place belongs to which show?

Places	TV Series
1. Ramsey Street	*Emmerdale Farm*
2. René's Cafe	*Are You Being Served?*
3. Kelsall Street	*Neighbours*

3. Depending on how well travelled you are, you might be able to match the following countries with the currency they use.

Countries	*Currencies*
1. France	Drachma
2. Japan	Schilling
3. South Africa	Mark
4. India	Rand
5. Bulgaria	Peseta
6. Germany	Franc
7. China	Rupee
8. Austria	Renminbi
9. Spain	Yen
10. Greece	Lev

4. Finally here's your chance to prove what a movie buff you are. Can you match the following films with their lead stars?

Films	Stars
1. *Raiders of the Lost Ark*	Mark Hammill
2. *Who Framed Roger Rabbit?*	Christopher Reeve
3. *Back To The Future*	Tom Hanks
4. *The Living Daylights*	Julie Andrews
5. *Superman*	Dudley Moore
6. *Mary Poppins*	Bob Hoskins
7. *Big*	Timothy Dalton
8. *Batman*	Harrison Ford
9. *Arthur*	Michael J. Fox
10. *Star Wars*	Michael Keaton

POP'S THE QUESTION

All the following questions are based on hit pop records over the past five years.

1. What did Curiosity kill on just another Ordinary Day?
2. Who should be so lucky?
3. Who are Craig, Luke and Matt?
4. Who advised never to trust a stranger with your heart?
5. Three girls were found guilty of love in the first degree. Who were they?
6. Billy Jean was not the lover of who?
7. Who were left to their own devices?
8. Who decided that the only way was up?
9. 'Anyone Can Fall In Love' by Anita Dobson was the theme song to which popular TV Soap Opera? Which character in the TV Show did Anita play?
10. Who warned her papa not to preach?
11. '*Je ne sais pourquoi*,' sang someone even though she wasn't French. Who was she and what nationality is she?
12. Who went downtown twenty years after her first excursion there?
13. Running up that Hill was the favourite sport of who?
14. '*Last Christmas*' someone gave his heart. Who was he?

15. Who wanted to party 'like it's 1999'?
16. It was a nice day for a white wedding for which singer?
17. Nasty Boys were especially liked by who?
18. Who wondered when they would be famous?
19. When this singer falls in love it will be forever. Who is he?
20. Who danced on the valentine in 1984 and were notorious in 1986?

WHERE IN THE WORLD?

Test your knowledge of geography with this specially devised quiz.

1. Name all seven continents.
2. In which country would you find the Rocky Mountains?
3. Which is the world's largest ocean?
4. Of which countries are the following the capital cities? a) New Delhi; b) The Hague; c) Paris; d) Washington; e) Madrid; f) Canberra.
5. Name four members of the EEC.
6. Is the Tropic of Cancer north or south of the Equator?
7. Which country is bordered by Sweden, Norway and the USSR?
8. Where would you find Nagasaki, Kyoto, Yokohama and Osaka?
9. In which countries are the following rivers? a) Amazon; b) Thames; c) Yangtse; d) Mississippi; e) Nile; f) Seine.
10. Which country is made up of two islands called North Island and South Island?

HISTORICAL HOWLERS

1. Who burnt the cakes?
2. Which English king had six wives? Give yourself an extra point if you can name all six of them and say what happened to each of them.
3. How many King Georges have there been on the British throne?
4. Which British monarch has reigned the longest?
5. Who conquered England in 1066, and which English king did he defeat?
6. Who was the son of Mary Queen of Scots who came to the throne in 1603 and became the first king of both England and Scotland?
7. Which British king gave up the throne in 1936 for the woman he loved?
8. For a short time Britain was ruled jointly by a King and Queen. Who were they?
9. Who was Queen of England for only nine days?
10. Name the next two Kings of Great Britain.

LITERACY LUNACY

All the following questions are taken from classic books you'll have read.

1. Which four children were crowned kings and queens by a lion after they helped to end a winter which had lasted a hundred years?
2. What sort of factory did Willy Wonka get himself involved with?
3. Who was Gandalf?
4. In what year did the Space Odyssey described by Arthur C. Clarke take place?
5. Dora and Steve were friends on which farm for retired horses?
6. How did Paddington Bear get his name and where did he come from originally?
7. Who wrote a secret diary when he was aged 13¾?
8. Who asked for some more?
9. A white rabbit consulting his pocket watch, Humpty Dumpty, and a talking caterpillar were all creatures encountered by which little girl?
10. In which books do the following characters appear? a) Wendy and the Lost Boys; b) Moriarty; c) Ebenezer Scrooge; d) The Queen of Hearts; e) Miss Lark's Andrew.

PROVERBIAL PUZZLERS

How well do you know your proverbs and old sayings? Test your knowledge of these ancient words of wisdom with the following questions.

1. If a red sky at night is a shepherd's delight, what does a red sky at morning signify?
2. What does one swallow not make?
3. What do April showers bring?
4. What is preferable to being sorry?
5. What should you never burn?
6. What should you never put off till tomorrow?
7. What is one man's meat to another man?
8. What does less haste usually bring?
9. What should never be put in one basket?
10. Absence makes what grow fonder?

IRRITATING INITIALS

Can you work out the most common meaning of the following initials?

1. UN
2. WHO
3. BBC
4. ITN
5. BA
6. CND
7. UNESCO
8. USSR
9. USA
10. AA
11. SRN
12. LWT
13. NATO
14. BT
15. BR   British Rail
16. RAC
17. LBW
18. BSc
19. OBE
20. HMSO
21. NW
22. H_2O
23. NSPCC
24. RSPCA

25. PTO
26. RAF
27. NHS
28. YMCA
29. MGM
30. DDT

ODD ONES OUT

Can you recognise which is the odd one out in the following groups of names; and then say why it is the odd one out? Most of these puzzles are reasonably straightforward – but a couple have a hidden twist to them!

1.
 apple
 orange
 pear
 peach
 pomegranate
 banana
 tangerine

2.
 Westminster Abbey
 St Paul's Cathedral
 Tower of London
 Hadrian's Wall
 The Eiffel Tower
 Canterbury Cathedral

3.
 daisy
 buttercup
 cactus
 rose

lily
orchid

4.
London
Edinburgh
Swansea
Dublin
Manchester
Belfast
Glasgow

5.
The Living Daylights
You Only Live Twice
Octopussy
Raiders of the Lost Ark
Goldfinger

6.
Wembley
St Annes
Blackpool
Wimbledon
The Oval

7.
Cliff Richard
Sting
Bruce Springsteen
Rick Astley
Nick Kamen

8.
Yorkshire
Pekinese

Siamese
Alsatian
Chihauhua

9.
hat
coat
scarf
skirt
shoes
jeans
gloves

10.
Brighton
Morecambe
Leicester
Blackpool
Scarborough
Margate

11.
King John
King George V
Queen Anne
King Edward VI
King Arthur
King Stephen
Queen Victoria

12.
oboe
piano
flute
recorder

trumpet
bassoon

13.
Argentina
New Zealand
Tasmania
Turkey
South Africa
Chile

14.
Doctor Who
Professor Challenger
Professor Branestawn
Albert Einstein

15.
gold
lead
mercury
tin
platinum
iron

16.
Adrian
Simon
Shifty
Joey
Aveline
Freddie

17.
 Australia
 Canada
 Asia
 South America
 Antarctica

18.
 George
 Charles
 Edward
 Peter
 Stephen
 John

19.
 1969
 1888
 1165
 1798
 1699
(*clue: none of the above is a date!*)

20.
 Yorkshire
 Lancashire
 Black
 Pease
 Christmas
 Plum

21.
 Ada
 Deed
 Sister

Pip
Madam

22.
Christmas Day
New Year's Day
Easter Monday
Thanksgiving
Good Friday

23.
RETEP
HARAS
LAUP
MAILLIW
NEK
LLESSUR
DIVAD

24.
hare
movie
cereal
tree
bee
spree
dance
oboe

25.
Romeo and Juliet
Henry VIII
Richard III
King John
Anthony and Cleopatra
George V

26.
  Thames
  Avon
  Mersey
  Clyde
  Humber
  Ouse

27.
  September
  February
  November
  June
  April

28.
  Jersey
  Sark
  Skye
  Guernsey
  Alderney

29.
  Albatross
  Dodo
  Emu
  Ostrich
  Raven
  Owl

30.
  Leo
  Gemini
  Scorpio
  Andromeda

CRAFTY
CROSSWORDS

Crossword Number One

ACROSS
 1. Eve ate this fruit (5).
 5. Insane (3).
 6. This is used in the garden to clear away dead leaves (4).
 8. You and me (2).
 9. Pronoun (2).
10. Present tense of the verb 'to be' (2).
12. You can cook with this, and you can also get it from the North Sea (3).
13. A worker on a building site might carry his bricks around in this (3).
14. These races are held annually in the Isle of Man (2).
15. British Rail (abbrev.) (2).
16. Football Association (abbrev.) (2).
17. This grows in the field (4).
18. Loud noise (3).
20. We have this apple in our throat (5).

DOWN
 2. Country neighbouring India (8).
 3. Los Angeles (abbrev.) (2).
 4. Secret British organisation, particularly adept at fighting terrorists (3).
 5. Type of edible fungus (8).
 6. Fury (4).
 7. He was told to phone home . . . (2).
11. Eve ate 1 across here (4).
15. Before Christ (abbrev.) (2).
16. Repair (3).
19. Anno Domini (abbrev.) (2).

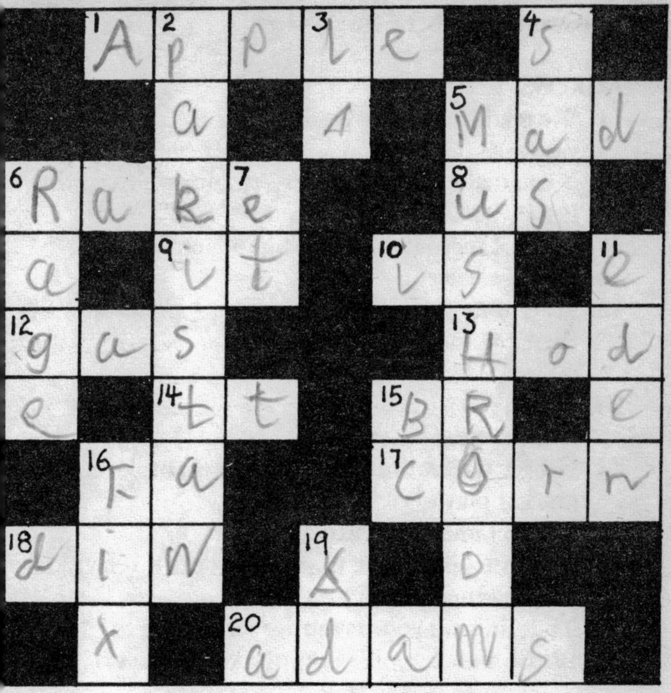

Crossword Number Two

ACROSS

1. We read from these on TV (7).
7. Cut (4).
8. If you make a successful pop record you'll get this (4).
9. Body of men on board a ship or aeroplane (4).
10. Microphone (4).
12. *Terry and June*, *'Allo 'Allo* and *Bread* are all these (3–4).

DOWN

2. Independent Television (abbrev.) (3).
3. *Oliver*, *Grease* and *Annie* are all examples of this kind of play (7).
4. You get one at Christmas (7).
5. You use this to tape your favourite television programmes (5).
6. You can hear your favourite records on this (5).
11. British Broadcasting Corporation (abbrev.) (3).

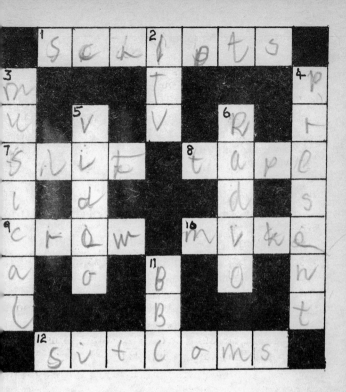

Across:
1. SCRIPTS
7. SLIFE
8. TAPE
9. CRAW
10. MIKE
12. SITCOMS

Crossword Number Three

ACROSS

1. A suit in a pack of cards (6).
3. Amateur Athletic Association (abbrev.) (3).
4. He is in charge of flying an aeroplane (5).
7. The 'one' in a pack of cards (3).
8. To push oneself to the limit (5).
10. Place (3).
11. Foe (5).
12. Word of affirmation (3).
13. Word for against, used mainly in sports (6).

DOWN

2. They are members of 3 across (8).
3. Not professionals (8).
5. Large animal, used as a beast of burden (2).
6. A golf ball is placed on this (3).
9. Royal Navy (abbrev.) (2).

Across

1. HEARTS
3. AAA
4. PILOT
7. ACE
8. EXERT
10. PUT
11. ENEMY
12. YES
13. VERSUS

Down

2. ATHLETE
5. OXE
6. TART
9. TRAIT

Crossword Number Four

ACROSS

1. You have to wear this when you ride a motor bike (5, 6).
9. Legendary character who killed all his wives (9).
10. The daughter of your brother or sister (5).
11. Boiling water will produce this, and trains used to depend for their power on this (5).
12. A lake in Cumbria — almost sounding like the name of a certain farm in a television series (9)!
13. Egg and ————; this is often played at school sports days (5,4).
16. English town (5).
17. We do this when we sleep (5).
19. Debates (9).
22. The top of the stairs (5, 4).
24. To come in (5).
26. Bring together (5).
27. Without any meaning or logic (9).
28. People in these shouldn't throw stones (5, 6)!

DOWN

1. A slide or a slope (5).
2. The white of an egg (7).
3. Pull up (5).
4. Puts into danger (9).
5. It's not animal and it's not vegetable. . . (7).
6. Everyone aged between thirteen and nineteen (9).
7. Birds found in Egypt, among other places (6).
8. Frenchmen, so we're told, wear these on their heads quite a lot (6)!
14. You may go into this theatre at the hospital (9).
15. These are found on the fronts of letters (9).

17. People make a sport out of throwing this (6).
18. Shortened form of the name Margery (5).
20. Not serving any purpose (7).
21. Indian women often wear these traditional dresses (5).
23. Type of Australian dog (5).
25. Oak, beech and ash (5).

Crossword Number Five

ACROSS

7. Another word for men (5).
8. A simple person from the American backwoods — four of them came to Beverly Hills (9).
9. You might find these on a cowboy's jacket (5).
10. Phil Collins is one — and so is Robert Redford (9).
12. Singer with the Eurythmics (5, 6).
16. Famous Brazilian footballer in the 1970s (4).
17. Spanish for 'Let's Go!' (5).
18. ——————— of Wight (4).
19. Rome is sometimes called by this name which implies that this town will always be there (7, 4).
22. Holiday resort in the Canary Islands (3, 5).
24. Monks may live here (5).
25. A railway seat, for example, which is set aside for someone (8).
26. Natives of Denmark (5).

DOWN

1. Dirty Den was one, and so is Dot Cotton (9).
2. These appear on the front pages of newspapers (9).
3. Your father may smoke one (4).
4. April the First (3, 5, 3).
5. Brighton, Blackpool and Southend all have them (5).
6. We spend about a third of our lives engaged in this activity (5).
11. Bryan Ferry was one in this song (5, 2, 4).
13. Someone who gives a name to something (5).
14. The staccato sound in some of your favourite dance records (5, 4).

15. You may feel like this when someone pays you an enormous compliment (9).
20. Monopoly, Trivial Pursuit and Snap are all examples of these (5).
21. Less haste, more ——— (5).
23. Boy's name, short for Andrew (4).

Crossword Number Six

ACROSS

5 and 26. This film featured a host of cartoon characters from Toontown (3, 6, 5, 6).

9. What you hopefully did after reading the jokes in this book (6).

10. You dial 100 on your telephone to get this person (8).

11. The first name of actress Miss Keith (8).

13. Tarzan and his jungle friends could be called this (3–3).

15. Robin Cousins is one and so is Chris Dean (6).

17. The first name of TV personality Miss Rantzen (6).

20. A result, or the consequence of something acting upon something else (6).

22. ——— *Beginners* was a film starring David Bowie and Patsy Kensit (8).

24. Santa has several of this creature (8).

26. See 5 across.

28. They were left to their own devices while domino dancing (3, 3, 4, 4).

DOWN

1. Duncan Goodhew is one of these sportsmen (8).

2. An illegal play in a football game (4).

3. Sideways on (8).

4. Girl's name and the Italian name of Italy's capital city (4).

6. You might hear Mike Reid, Mike Smith – or even Phillip Scofield – on this (5).

7. Bobby, the footballer, and an Old Almanac (6).

8. The sea and the wind can do this to the coastline slowly over millions of years (5).

12. You do this to a mistake in your exercize book (5).
14. Girl's name (5).
16. Pleads for (8).
18. Attempts again (7).
19. It grows on your head (4).
21. A refrigerator will keep your food in this condition (5).
23. Sticky liquid you can pour on waffles (5).
25. The back of your neck (4).
27. A ghost might say this to you (3)!

WACKY WORDS

TOPS AND TAILS

In each of the following puzzles *three* answers are required for each question (sorry about this but you can't say you're not getting value for money!). The word in brackets, indicated by a long dash, forms both the last part of the first word, and the first part of the last word, and is always something connected with a sport or a game.

For instance, the answer to question 1 is bat: a vampire *bat* is a blood-sucking mammal; and *Bat*man is the superhero of Gotham City. Now see how well you get on with the others!

1. Blood-sucking mammal (—) Superhero of Gotham City.
2. Game played at Wembley (—) Usually brightly-coloured, made of rubber and floating at the end of a string.
3. Data entered into a computer (—) Used to fix a sheet of glass to a window frame.
4. Flower (—) Mother Hubbard's was bare.
5. It crosses the Thames (—) Capital of Barbados.
6. The Beatles came from here (—) You can win a lot on these!
7. Strawberries come in one at the greengrocer's (—) Prickly plant.
8. Red, orange, yellow, green, blue, indigo and violet are its colours (—) Type of hat.

9. Of small width (—) Plant from which starch can be obtained.
10. Japanese warlord (—) German boy's name.

This time the word in brackets is either a boy's or a girl's name.

11. To poke (—) A rat or a mouse, for example.
12. To remove the top of milk, for example (—) Japanese garment.
13. The smallest part of matter (—) Weapon of a Red Indian.
14. Excuse me! (—) Give.
15. District in India and a type of tea (—) Biblical figure who lost his strength when his hair was cut.

16. European country (—) Place where things are bought and sold.
17. This can be put into a slot machine (—) Type of Japanese fencing.
18. Type of herb (—) American state.
19. Paving material often used on roads (—) Firm of purpose.
20. Name for the Devil (—) Early type of jukebox.

WORD IN THE MIDDLE

In the following puzzle the brackets represent a word which, when added to the end of the first word, and added to the beginning of the second word makes two more words. In question 1, for instance, if you add the word ICE to PRACT you will get PRACTICE, and if you add it to BERG you get ICEBERG. Now see if you can do the others!

1. PRACT (...............) BERG
2. HAIL (...............) WORK
3. FAT (...............) MIT
4. RELI (...............) NTUAL
5. GER (...............) OR
6. JIG (...............) MILL
7. A (...............) LEMAN
8. CHRIST (...............) TER
9. SO (...............) PLE
10. CINE (...............) RROW

MANIC MEANINGS

This may look the same as the previous puzzle but in fact it's quite different. This time it's up to you to find the word in brackets which means the same as the two words outside the brackets. For instance, the missing word in the question FISH (...............) ONLY would be SOLE: a sole is a fish and it also means 'only'. See how you get on with these.

1. PAUSE (...............) DESTROY
2. ABLE TO (...............) TIN
3. BIRD (...............) MIMIC
4. ANGRY (...............) INSANE
5. SKIN (...............) CONCEAL
6. STICK (...............) CONFECTION
7. DIRECT (...............) CATTLE
8. ENCOURAGEMENT (...............) STRUT
9. FORBID (...............) ROD
10. FINAL (...............) ENDURE

VANISHING VOWELS

In these puzzles *all* the vowels and spaces have been taken out of the titles of famous movies. Can you work out what they are?

1. GRMLNS (2 vowels missing)
2. THMPRSTRKSBCK (7 vowels missing)
3. WHFRMDRGRRBBT? (7 vowels missing)
4. CSBLNC (4 vowels missing)
5. THWZRDFZ (5 vowels missing)

The following are all the titles of famous books which you have probably read:

6. THLNTHWTCHNDTHWRDRB (10 vowels missing)
7. BLKHS (5 vowels missing)
8. THWNDNTHWLLWS (6 vowels missing)
9. THDRYFNNFRNK (7 vowels missing)
10. THSCRTDRYFDRNML (11 vowels missing)

In the next series all the vowels have been taken out of well-known proverbs or sayings:

11. BSNCMKSTHHRTGRWFNDR (11 vowels missing)

12. CRSTYKLLDTHCT (8 vowels missing)
13. STLLWTRSRNDP (6 vowels missing)
14. HNSTYSTHBSTPLCY (7 vowels missing)
15. TFSGHTTFMND (8 vowels missing)

And finally all the vowels have been taken out of the opening lines of popular nursery rhymes:

16. HWMNYMLSTBBYLN? (7 vowels missing)
17. FRNDTWNTYBLCKBRDS (6 vowels missing)
18. JCKSPRTTCLDTNFT (8 vowels missing)

19. PTRPPRPCKDPCKFPCKLDPPPR (13 vowels missing)
20. RNGRNGFRSS (6 vowels missing)

ENDS. . .

Your job in the next set of word puzzles is to find the letters which, when added to each one of the preceding letters or groups of letters given, will give you another word. For instance, if you were given the letters P, T, F, C and W, the answer would be OOL, as when OOL is added to each of the letters in turn a new word is formed (pool, tool, fool, cool, wool). Now see how you do with these (a hint is that it's always best to start with the word with the most letters!):

1. T =
   B =
   D =
   F =
   H =
   Y =
   END =

2. D =
   B =
   PREP =
   H =
   C =
   F =

3. R =

S =
SL =
M =
EYEBR =

4. P =
   HE =
   ST =
   W =
   C =

5. G =
   L =
   M =
   N =
   R =
   HE =
   SL =

. . . AND BEGINNINGS

This next puzzle is the same as the other one — but the other way round (!). This time you have to find the word which, when put in front of the following letters, makes another word:

1. = EEP
   = AVE
   = INK
   = OPE
   = ANT

2. = OWN
   = INK
   = AVE
   = EAK
   = AWL

3. = ING
   = ONG
   = IRD
   = REE
   = ROW

4. = ONE
   = ONG
   = WAYS
   = PINE

= TER

. = AT
= MBLE
= E
= ASON

WHAT COMES NEXT?

These following puzzles are very similar to numbe
puzzles, but instead of guessing which number logi
cally comes next, you have to guess which letter. I
will probably help you if you write out the alphabe
first on a scrap piece of paper, but be warned —
couple are particularly nasty and devious!

1. A E I O .....
2. B C D F .....
3. A B D G K P .....
4. B D F H J .....
5. Z Y W T P K .....
6. F H K M P R .....
7. T Q N K H .....
8. D H L P T .....
9. G R D N T H G P .....
10. P I L P C O I .....

BACK TO FRONT

Each set of the following clues has two answers; in each case the answer to the first clue will give you the answer to the second if you reverse the word. For instance, if the two clues were (*a*) *A boy's name* and (*b*) *A movement of the head*, the answers would be *Don* and *nod*, as when the word *Don* is read backwards it gives you *nod*. Now try these:

1. (a) Game played with cuesticks and balls.
   (b) Circle.

2. (a) A man's best friend.
   (b) The supreme being.

3. (a) Used for frying food in.
   (b) Sleep.

4. (a) Section of a hospital.
   (b) Illustrate.

5. (a) Someone who doesn't tell the truth.
   (b) A train can travel on one.

WANDERING
WORDS

1. In the following grid are hidden twenty words, each of which has something to do with television. Can you find them all? Some of the words are spelt backwards, some are written horizontally and some vertically!

To help you the words are:

COMEDY	PRESENTER	RADIO
SOAP OPERA	PRODUCER	CAMERAMAN
THRILLER	STAR	EDITOR
MAKE-UP	BBC	ROLE
VIDEO	DIRECTOR	ITV
CHANNEL	TESTCARD	FILM
BROADCAST		

```
P W Q R F G P R O D U C E R U
F R B H I B R S W K L A O O L
T H R I L L E R G F D M W L H
E F F F M G S E E E E E E E E
S S S H J I E D I T O R R T H
T Y O A Q W N H Y I P A W E R
C R A I I I T V B C O M E D Y
A Q P E R A E A S B A A W I H
R F O I D A R G G B S N N R T
D F P E R T H K O H G D D E E
I O E D I V R L E N N A H C C
A S R Y Y U U I O H E R R T Y
W M A K E U P F G H W O O O O
Q T I L K G V B N M S T A R R
A B R O A D C A S T T I M F D
```

2. In this one the words all have something to do with astronomy or space travel.

NEBULA   MARS   CAPE
ROCKETS   NOVA   KENNEDY
SATURN   QUASAR   MERCURY
SHUTTLE   EARTH   VENUS
             RACE   URANUS
                       SUN
                       MOON

```
C A P E K E N N E D Y E Q W S
Q L O L O L O G H J E T H J S
Q U E F V B V E N U S C D X E
D B N W Z Z A D F G H J K U N
A E Y I W Q R Y U S R A M E U
A N D V E W Q W E R T E T T
W Q E R Y E R T G H S D R I P
W Y O P G F R Y U I P A C X E
E R O C K E T S Q S A T U R N
A A E O J N F E E E C S R A C
A S U N F P E R A C E W Y O P
A A S D F L R E R S R R R R R
Q U R A N U S E T A S A S S S
A Q S D Y T S S H U T T L E E
A Q K M O O N F G T J S W E R
```

3. The following are all names of boys and girls.

GORDON	RICHARD	SARAH
PHILLIP	PETER	ANDY
HORACE	ED	ALEXIS
JEAN	STUART	GARY
TRACEY	TOM	MICHAEL
LEE	SHARON	ROY
PENNY	CATHY	UNA
ADRIAN	DAN	PIP

```
A W C Z Z X D H U I O L J U U
L E E W Q N N A I R D A A A A
E H H T S E A N F E W N A A A
A U G T I S D W T R A U T S W
H A F G X E Q W T P G F D A Q
C D F J E A N V R I C H A R D
I D F G L W Q Y T L S Q A A A
M O T A A N D Y L L O N F H H
A S R F F O I I I I F O F F F
R R A W R D G H J H O R A C E
A S C D E R E T E P G A A A A
A S E O O O S S D W W H D T X
A S Y R A G V P D F G S S H T
A S D O R T Y I D W R T Y Y Y
Z X X Y N N E P J J J J N R R
```

4. The following all have something to do with music and records.

SAXOPHONE   SYNTHESIZER   TAPE
HIT   CHARTS   LP
OPERA   HIP-HOP   RECORD
BAND   DRUMS   PIANO
BASS   CD   DEMO
SINGER   DJ   SOLO
SINGLE   MIKE   TOP OF THE
DISCO   POPS

```
S A T A F G B H U I P E T D G
A X A S D R U M S D S S S S S
X U P A N D F G H J O C S I D
O P E R A S D F G H L N O N N
P A D F B A S S E R O G G G G
H I T F G H I G T R P P F L S
O D F B S Y N T H E S I Z E R
N G H O R A G G Z X X A S S E
E P J D D F E Q W H B N A C C
A T H C H A R T S O F O G G O
Q W E R I F G H J U T R E E R
A W E R P Q E R Y H D D D D D
W H Y O H G E T M I K E Q W E
E R Y H O L L F G H J M S D F
A G B S P O P E H T F O P O T
```

107

5. And just to make things difficult there are no clues as to what the following eleven words have in common!

```
Q W B I G S M Q W C R G T H B
A F G R H O A S W E R T G H A
T H E S O U N D O F M U S I C
A W H T S D F G H J J J J J K
A W R T F F F G C C A W R T
Q W B B B B P I N O C C H I O
A S D F U E W W W C C C O O T
G R E Y S T O K E A O A S D H
A S D F T T T T G G C C O O E
A S D F E E E Z X C O O Z X F
A S T A R W A R S A F G B U U
T H E S S R T E L E P H A N T
A S D F G H J K L U U M M M U
A S D F G J K Y T R R B B B R
Y E L L O W S U B M A R I N E
```

FRANTIC FIGURES

ODD EVENS AND EVEN ODDS

In this puzzle you have to work out which number in the sequence is the odd one out. For instance in the sequence 4 8 9 16 32, the odd one out would be 9 because it is the only number which isn't an even number or which isn't a multiple of 4.

See how you get on with these:

1. 4 28 16 24428 13 22
2. 9 3 6 12 16 15
3. 21 39 35 56 14
4. 33 42 91 60 24
5. 66 5331 71 1191 93
6. 16 45 32 64 88
7. 3 9 55 42 43 123
8. 5 25 87 95 150
9. 52 70 1511 61 16 25
10. 50 1040 1000 156 70 330

NUMBING NUMBERS

In this quiz it's up to you to work out which number comes next in the given sequence. For instance, in the sequence 5 10 15 20 25, the next number is obviously 30 as each number is a multiple of 5. In the sequence 8 9 11 14, the next number would be 18 — the second number is one more than the previous number, the second is two more and so on. Easy, isn't it?

But watch out — some of these are a little more devious than others! And some are a *lot* more devious!!

1. 4 8 12 16 20
2. 1 2 3 4 5 6
3. 64 32 16 8 4
4. 3 6 9 15 24
5. 33 44 55 66
6. 20 17 14 11 8
7. 12 14 18 26 42
8. 49 42 35 28 21
9. 16 19 25 34
10. 3 9 81 6561
11. 34 29 25 22 20
12. 7 11 15 19 23
13. 5 7 12 19 31 50
14. 637 605 573 541
15. 4 7 11 16 22
16. 18 13 9 6
17. 3 6 18 72

18. 6 13 27 55 111
19. 9 18 27 36
20. 8 15 23 31

DOTTY DIGITS

The two following number grids work on the same principle as the word grids you did before. Hidden in the grids are the answers to the sums.

In the grids none of the answers is interconnected and they are all read horizontally from left to right.

1.

$13 + 16 =$
$22 \div 2 =$
$13 + 49 + 3 =$
$39 - 18 =$
$8 \times 16 =$
$1 \times 30 =$
$49 + 67 =$
$12 \div 3 =$

2	0	7	8	3	8	0	0	0	0
2	1	0	7	7	7	1	2	8	1
2	8	2	1	1	6	6	7	6	0
5	5	5	7	9	0	2	2	4	0
2	2	2	8	8	6	5	7	7	7
5	6	6	5	6	2	9	8	9	9
6	6	9	8	0	1	2	8	7	3
3	3	1	2	7	5	5	6	6	6
3	5	6	7	8	6	5	7	3	2
1	1	8	7	8	8	8	8	1	1

2.

$60 \times 22 =$
$25 - 16 =$
$608 \div 4 = 152$
$33 + 671 =$
$1444 - 16 =$
$13 \times 2 =$
$144 \div 12 =$
$22 + 1 =$

0	0	2	3	7	8	0	1	0	2
1	3	2	0	3	3	1	4	2	8
1	2	2	2	2	2	3	7	1	5
2	6	2	2	2	2	2	3	2	2
1	6	8	7	8	9	0	6	7	8
2	2	3	4	4	4	4	4	4	3
7	0	7	7	0	8	7	0	4	7
1	5	2	2	5	4	5	5	5	5
1	3	3	2	3	2	2	1	0	1
9	1	1	1	1	1	4	4	4	4

BRAIN TEASERS

LOONY LOGIC

1. It's Christmas time and Gary, John, Fiona, Lee, Alison and Nick have all been given record tokens. They went down to the record shop and bought records by Kim Wilde, Bananarama, Rick Astley, the Pet Shop Boys, Beethoven and Madonna.

Can you tell from the following clues who bought what?

1. Gary chose a record by a solo girl singer.
2. John hates pop music and got the record he wanted.
3. Lee chose a girl singer, but not Kim Wilde.
4. Alison and Nick both chose records by groups.
5. Nick chose the Pet Shop Boys.

2. In this year's Miss World contest, the top eight nations were New Zealand, East Germany, Brazil, Switzerland, the United Kingdom, Austria, Norway and France.

In which order did they finish?

1. New Zealand was three places behind the only other English-speaking country and four places ahead of Brazil.
2. France was beaten by East Germany, but the French girl beat the New Zealand girl.
3. Norway was beaten by Austria but was placed above Switzerland.

3. It's the height of summer and Tracey, Johnathan, Helen, Denise, Stuart and Elaine are all off on holiday. Back home their mutual friend got postcards from the USA, Australia, Spain, Blackpool, Greece and Iceland. But all of them were unsigned! Can you work out who went where?

1. Neither Tracey nor Elaine had a holiday in a European country.
2. Only Helen had to pack very warm clothing.
3. Only Tracey crossed the Equator.
4. Denise took only a train to her destination.
5. Stuart flew to Athens airport.

4. In the school orchestra Diane, Nikki, Tony, Jackie and Sean are all chosen to play. Their choice of instruments is a synthesizer, a piano, an oboe, a guitar and a violin. Who plays what?

1. Tony cannot play any stringed instrument.
2. Diane plays the piano.
3. Nikki plays a stringed instrument but not a guitar.
4. Tony doesn't play a wind instrument.
5. Sean uses a plectrum to play his instrument.

5. Simon, Jane, Martin, Laura and Mary all took part enthusiastically in the schools sports day. The sports they took part in were: 100 metres, gymnastics, discus-throwing, javelin-throwing and swimming. From the following clues can you work out who played which sport and in what overall place they finished at the end of the day?

1. Laura came third, and her specialist sport involved her throwing something.
2. Simon came above Laura, but below Martin.
3. Jane beat Mary who was a gymnast.

119

4. Jane was involved in a race but cannot swim.
5. Martin threw the discus.

ANSWERS AT LAST!

QUIRKY QUIZZES
MATCH TO MATCH

1. 1. Decathlon – Daley Thompson; 2. Running – Zola Budd; 3. Skiing – Eddie Edwards; 4. Ice-skating – Jayne Torville; 5. Cricket – Imran Khan; 6. Boxing – Mike Tyson; 7. Javelin – Fatima Whitbread; 8. Football – Gary Lineker; 9. Snooker – Steve Davis; 10. Swimming – Duncan Goodhew.

2. 1. Ramsey Street – *Neighbours*; 2. René's Café – *'Allo 'Allo*; 3. Kelsall Street – *Bread*; 4. Albert Square – *EastEnders*; 5. Gallifrey – *Doctor Who*; 6. Gotham City – *Batman*; 7. The Woolpack – *Emmerdale Farm*; 8. Maplin's Holiday Camp – *Hi-De-Hi*; 9. Grace Brothers' Department Store – *Are You Being Served?*; 10. The Rover's Return – *Coronation Street*.

3. 1. France – Franc; 2. Japan – Yen; 3. South Africa – Rand; 4. India – Rupee; 5. Bulgaria – Lev; 6. Germany – Mark; 7. China – Renminbi; 8. Austria – Schilling; 9. Spain – Peseta; 10. Greece – Drachma.

4. 1. *Raiders Of The Lost Ark* – Harrison Ford; 2. *Who Framed Roger Rabbit?* – Bob Hoskins; 3. *Back to the Future* – Michael J Fox; 4. *The Living Daylights* – Timothy Dalton; 5. *Superman* – Christopher Reeve; 6. *Mary Poppins* – Julie Andrews; 7. *Big* – Tom Hanks; 8. *Batman* – Michael Keaton; 9. *Arthur* – Dudley Moore; 10. *Star Wars* – Mark Hammill.

POP'S THE QUESTION

1. Curiosity Killed The Cat.
2. Kylie Minogue.
3. Bros.
4. Kim Wilde.
5. Bananarama.
6. Michael Jackson.
7. The Pet Shop Boys.
8. Yazz and the Plastic Population.
9. *EastEnders*; she played the part of Angie Watts.
10. Madonna.
11. Kylie Minogue; she's Australian.
12. Petula Clark.
13. Kate Bush.
14. George Michael.
15. Prince.
16. Billy Idol.
17. Janet Jackson.
18. Bros.
19. Rick Astley.
20. Duranduran.

WHERE IN THE WORLD?

1. Asia, Africa, Australasia, North America, South America, Antarctica, Europe.
2. The USA.
3. The Pacific Ocean.
4. a) India; b) Holland; c) France; d) The USA; e) Spain; f) Australia.
5. The United Kingdom, France, West Germany, Spain, Portugal, Greece, Belgium, Luxembourg, Eire, Holland, Denmark, Italy.
6. North.
7. Finland.
8. In Japan.

9. a) Brazil; b) England; c) China; d) USA;
   e) Egypt; f) France.
10. New Zealand.

HISTORICAL HOWLERS
1. King Alfred.
2. Henry VIII. His wives were: Catherine of Aragon
   whom he divorced; Anne Boleyn who was
   beheaded; Jane Seymour who died shortly after
   giving birth; Anne of Cleves whom he divorced;
   Catherine Howard who was beheaded; and
   Catherine Parr who survived Henry.
3. Six.
4. Queen Victoria. She reigned for sixty-four years,
   from 1837 to 1901.
5. William the Conquerer. He defeated and killed
   King Harold.
6. James I.
7. Edward VIII.
8. William and Mary.
9. Lady Jane Grey.
10. The next two kings of Great Britain will be the
    Queen's son, Prince Charles, and his son, Prince
    William.

LITERARY LUNACY
1. Peter, Susan, Edmund and Lucy Pevensie in *The
   Lion, The Witch and The Wardrobe*.
2. A chocolate factory.
3. The magician who appears in *The Hobbit* and
   The Lord of the Rings.
4. 2001.
5. Follyfoot.
6. He was called Paddington because he was found

at Paddington; he came originally from darkest Peru.
7. Adrian Mole.
8. Oliver Twist.
9. Alice in *Alice's Adventures in Wonderland* and *Through the Looking Glass*.
10. a) Peter Pan; b) The Sherlock Holmes stories; c) A Christmas Carol; d) Alice's Adventures in Wonderland; e) Mary Poppins.

PROVERBIAL PUZZLERS
1. Shepherd's (or sailor's) warning.
2. One swallow does not make a summer.
3. May flowers.
4. Better safe than sorry.
5. Never burn your bridges.
6. Never put off till tomorrow what you can do today.
7. One man's meat is another man's poison.
8. Less haste, more speed.
9. Never put all your eggs in one basket.
10. Absence makes the heart grow fonder.

IRRITATING INITIALS
1. United Nations; 2. World Health Organization; 3. British Broadcasting Corporation; 4. Independent Television News; 5. British Airways *or* Bachelor of Arts; 6. Campaign for Nuclear Disarmament; 7. United Nations Educational Scientific and Cultural Organization; 8. Union of Soviet Socialist Republics; 9. United States of America; 10. Alcoholics Anonymous *or* Automobile Association; 11. State Registered Nurse; 12. London Weekend Television; 13. North Atlantic Treaty Organization; 14. British Telecom; 15. British Rail; 16. Royal Automobile Club; 17. Leg

Before Wicket (in cricket); 18. Bachelor of Science; 19. Order of the British Empire; 20. Her Majesty's Stationery Office; 21. North-West; 22. The chemical symbol for water; 23. National Society for the Prevention of Cruelty to Children; 24. Royal Society for the Prevention of Cruelty to Animals; 25. Please Turn Over (at the bottom of a page of a letter); 26. Royal Air Force; 27. National Health Service; 28. Young Men's Christian Association; 29. Metro-Goldwyn-Meyer (the film company); 30. Dichlorodiphenyltrichloroethane, an insecticide (and if you got this one right you're either a genius, or you cheated!!!).

ODD ONES OUT

1. Banana – all the rest are round-shaped fruits.
2. The Eiffel Tower – all the other tourist attractions are in Britain.
3. Cactus – all the rest are flowering plants.
4. Dublin – all the rest are cities in the United Kingdom; Dublin is in Ireland.
5. *Raiders of the Lost Ark* – all the rest are James Bond films.
6. Blackpool – all the rest are the locations for famous sporting events.
7. Bruce Springsteen – all the rest are British singers.
8. Siamese – all the rest are breeds of dog; a Siamese is a breed of cat.
9. Skirt – the others are items of clothing which can be worn by either boys or girls.
10. Leicester – all the rest are seaside resorts.
11. King Arthur – he is the only fictional person in this list of kings and queens.
12. Piano – all the rest are wind instruments.
13. Turkey – it is the only country mentioned which is in the northern hemisphere.

14. Albert Einstein – all the rest are fictional scientists.

15. Mercury – it is the only metal mentioned which is liquid at room temperature.

16. Simon – all the rest are the first names of members of the Boswell family in the TV series *Bread*.

17. Canada – all the rest are continents.

18. Peter – all the rest are the names of kings.

19. 1165 – all the other numbers, when their individual digits are added together, make 25.

20. Lancashire – all the rest are types of puddings.

21. Sister – all the other words are palindromes. ie. they read the same backwards as well as forwards.

22. Thanksgiving – it is the only holiday not celebrated in Britain, but in the USA.

23. HARAS – when read backwards it forms Sarah, the only girl's name in the list.

24. Cereal – it is the only word which does not end in a vowel.

25. *George V* – all the others are titles of plays by William Shakespeare.

26. Clyde – all the rest are rivers in England.

27. February – all the other months have thirty days, February has twenty-eight and twenty-nine every Leap Year.

28. Skye – all the others form part of the Channel Islands.

29. Dodo – this is the only bird listed which is extinct.

30. Andromeda – every name listed here is a constellation but Andromeda is the only one which isn't one of the twelve signs of the Zodiac.

CRAFTY CROSSWORDS

Crossword 1.
ACROSS: 1. apple; 5. mad; 6. rake; 8. us; 9. it; 10. is; 12. gas; 13. hod; 14. TT; 15. BR; 16. FA; 17. corn; 18. din; 20. Adam's.
DOWN: 2. Pakistan; 3. LA; 4. SAS; 5. mushroom; 6. rage; 7. ET; 11. Eden; 15. BC; 16. fix; 19. AD.

Crossword 2.
ACROSS: 1. scripts; 7. snip; 8. fame; 9. crew; 10. mike; 12. sit-coms.
DOWN: 2. ITV; 3. musical; 4. present; 5. video; 6. radio; 11. BBC.

Crossword 3.
ACROSS: 1. hearts; 3. AAA; 4. pilot; 7. ace; 8. exert; 10. put; 11. enemy; 12. yes; 13. versus.
DOWN: 2. athletes; 3. amateurs; 5. ox; 6. tee; 9. RN.

Crossword 4.
ACROSS: 1. crash helmet; 9. Bluebeard; 10. niece; 11. steam; 12. Ennerdale; 13. spoon race; 16. Leeds; 17. dream; 19. discusses; 22. stair head; 24. enter; 26. unite; 27. senseless; 28. glass houses.
DOWN: 1. chute; 2. albumen; 3. heave; 4. endangers; 5. mineral; 6. teenagers; 7. ibises; 8. berets; 14. operating; 15. addresses; 17. discus; 18. Marge; 20. useless; 21. saris; 23. dingo; 25. trees.

Crossword 5.
ACROSS: 7. males; 8. hillbilly; 9. studs; 10. performer; 12. Annie Lennox; 16. Pele; 17. vamos; 18. isle; 19 Eternal City; 22. Las Palmas; 24. abbey; 25.

reserved; 26. Danes.
DOWN: 1. EastEnder; 2. headlines; 3. pipe; 4. All
Fools' Day; 5. piers; 6. sleep; 11. *Slave To Love*; 13.
namer; 14. disco beat; 15. flattered; 20. games; 21.
speed; 23. Andy.

Crossword 6.
ACROSS: 5. *Who Framed Roger*; 9. smiled; 10.
operator; 11. Penelope; 13. ape men; 15. skater; 17.
Esther; 20. effect; 22. Absolute; 24. reindeer; 26.
Rabbit; 28. The Pet Shop Boys.
DOWN: 1. swimmers; 2. foul; 3. edgeways; 4.
Roma; 6. radio; 7. Moores; 8. erode; 12. erase; 14.
Ethel; 16. entreats; 18. retries; 19. hair; 21. fresh;
23. syrup; 25. nape; 27. boo.

WACKY WORDS

TOPS AND TAILS
1. Vampire *bat (bat) Bat*man
2. Foot*ball (ball) Ball*oon
3. In*put (put) Put*ty
4. Butter*cup (cup) Cup*board
5. London *Bridge (Bridge) Bridge*town
6. Liver*pool (pool) Pool*s
7. Pun*net (net) Net*tle
8. Rain*bow (bow) Bow*ler
9. N*arrow (arrow) arrow*root
10. Sho*gun (gun) Gun*ter.
11. Pro*d (Rod) Rod*ent
12. S*kim (Kim) Kim*ono
13. A*tom (Tom) Tom*ahawk
14. Par*don (Don) Don*ate
15. As*sam (Sam) Sam*son
16. Den*mark (Mark) Mark*et
17. To*ken (Ken) Ken*do
18. Rose*mary (Mary) Mary*land
19. Tarmac*adam (Adam) Adam*ant
20. Old *Nick (Nick) Nick*elodeon.

WORD IN THE MIDDLE
1. PRACT (ICE) BERG
2. HAIL (STONE) WORK
3. FAT (HER) MIT
4. RELI (EVE) NTUAL
5. GER (MAN) OR
6. JIG (SAW) MILL
7. A (GENT) LEMAN
8. CHRIST (MAS) TER
9. SO (AP) PLE
10. CINE (MA) RROW

MANIC MEANINGS

1. BREAK
2. CAN
3. PARROT
4. MAD
5. HIDE
6. JAM
7. STEER
8. SPUR
9. BAR
10. LAST

VANISHING VOWELS

1. *Gremlins.*
2. *The Empire Strikes Back.*
3. *Who Framed Roger Rabbit?*
4. *Casablanca.*
5. *The Wizard of Oz.*
6. *The Lion, The Witch and The Wardrobe.*
7. *Bleak House.*
8. *The Wind In The Willows.*
9. *The Diary of Anne Frank.*
10. *The Secret Diary of Adrian Mole.*
11. Absence Makes the Heart Grow Fonder.
12. Curiosity Killed The Cat.
13. Still Waters Run Deep.
14. Honesty Is The Best Policy.
15. Out Of Sight, Out Of Mind.
16. How many Miles To Babylon?
17. Four And Twenty Blackbirds.
18. Jack Spratt Could Eat No Fat.
19. Peter Piper Pecked A Peck Of Pickled Pepper.
20. Ring A Ring Of Roses.

ENDS. . .
1. Tear; bear; dear; fear; hear; year; endear.
2. Dare; bare; prepare; hare; care; fare.
3. Row; sow; slow; mow; eyebrow.
4. Part; heart; start; wart; cart.
5. Gap; lap; map; nap; rap; heap; slap.

. . .AND BEGINNINGS
1. Sleep; slave; slink; slope; slant.
2. Brown; brink; brave; break; brawl.
3. Thing; thong; third; three; throw.
4. Alone; along; always; Alpine; alter.
5. Treat; tremble; tree; treason.

WHAT COMES NEXT?
1. U. This is a list of all the vowels in the alphabet.
2. G. G is the next consonant in the alphabet.
3. V. B is the next letter after A; D is the next but one letter after B; G is the third letter after D; and so on. V is the sixth letter after P.
4. L. Each letter is the next but one letter to the letter preceding it in the puzzle.
5. E. This is exactly the same as puzzle 3 except that, instead of going forwards in the alphabet we've gone backwards!
6. T. This is a nasty one but in fact it's just the same as puzzle 4, except that we've missed out any vowels we've come across.
7. E. If you go backwards through the alphabet you'll see that each letter is three letters down from the letter which precedes it in the list.
8. X. Each letter is four letters on from the letter which precedes it in the list.
—And as I did promise you a couple of really nasty and devious ones:

9. H. This is just 'Gordon The Gopher' with all the vowels taken out (sorry, Gordon!).
10. L. This is my name, Phillip Schofield, with every second letter omitted!

BACK TO FRONT
1. (a) pool; (b) loop.
2. (a) dog; (b) God.
3. (a) pan; (b) nap.
4. (a) ward; (b) draw.
5. (a) liar; (b) rail.

WANDERING WORDS

1.

```
P W Q R F G P R O D U C E R U
F R B H I B R S W K L A O O L
T H R I L L E R G F D M W L H
E F F F M G S E E E E E E E E
S S S H J I E D I T O R R T H
T Y O A Q W N H Y I P A W E R
C R A I I I T V B C O M E D Y
A Q P E R A E A S B A A W I H
R F O I D A R G G B S N N R T
D F P E R T H K O H G D D E E
I O E D I V R L E N N A H C C
A S R Y Y U U I O H E R R T Y
W M A K E U P F G H W O O O O
Q T I L K G V B N M S T A R R
A B R O A D C A S T T I M F D
```

134

2.

C	A	P	E	K	E	N	N	E	D	Y	E	Q	W	S
Q	L	O	L	O	L	O	G	H	J	E	T	H	J	S
Q	U	E	F	V	B	V	E	N	U	S	C	D	X	E
D	B	N	W	Z	Z	A	D	F	G	H	J	K	U	N
A	E	Y	I	W	Q	R	Y	U	S	R	A	M	E	U
A	N	D	W	V	E	W	Q	W	E	R	T	E	T	T
W	Q	E	R	Y	E	R	T	G	H	S	D	R	I	P
W	Y	O	P	G	F	R	Y	U	I	P	A	C	X	E
E	R	O	C	K	E	T	S	Q	S	A	T	U	R	N
A	A	E	O	J	N	F	E	E	E	C	S	R	A	C
A	S	U	N	F	P	E	R	A	C	E	W	Y	O	P
A	A	S	D	F	L	R	E	R	S	R	R	R	R	R
Q	U	R	A	N	U	S	E	T	A	S	A	S	S	S
A	Q	S	D	Y	T	S	S	H	U	T	T	L	E	E
A	Q	K	M	O	O	N	F	G	T	J	S	W	E	R

3.

```
A W C Z Z X D H U I O L J U L
L E E W Q N N A I R D A A A A
E H H T S E A N F E W N A A A
A U G T I S D W T R A U T S W
H A F G X E Q W T P G F D A Q
C D F J E A N V R I C H A R D
I D F G L W Q Y T L S Q A A A
M O T A A N D Y L L O N F H F
A S R F F O I I I I F O F F F
R R A W R D G H J H O R A C E
A S C D E R E T E P G A A A A
A S E O O O S S D W W H D T X
A S Y R A G V P D F G S S H T
A S D O R T Y I D W R T Y Y Y
Z X X Y N N E P J J J J N R R
```

136

4.

```
S A T A F G B H U I P E T D G
A X A S D R U M S D S S S S S
X U P A N D F G H J O C S I D
O P E R A S D F G H L N O N N
P A D F B A S S E R O G G G G
H I T F G H I G T R P P F L S
O D F B S Y N T H E S I Z E R
N G H O R A G G Z X X A S S E
E P J D D F E Q W H B N A C C
A T H C H A R T S O F O G G O
Q W E R I F G H J U T R E E R
A W E R P Q E R Y H D D D D D
W H Y O H G E T M I K E Q W E
E R Y H O L L F G H J M S D F
A G B S P O P E H T F O P O T
```

5.

```
Q W B I G S M Q W C R G T H B
A F G R H O A S W E R T G H A
T H E S O U N D O F M U S I C
A W H T S D F G H J J J J J K
A W R T T F F F G C C A W R T
Q W B B B B P I N O C C H I O
A S D F U E W W W C C C O O T
G R E Y S T O K E A O A S D H
A S D F T T T T G G C C O O E
A S D F E E E Z X C O O Z X F
A S T A R W A R S A F G B U U
T H E S S R T E L E P H A N T
A S D F G H J K L U U M M M U
A S D F G J K Y T R R B B B R
Y E L L O W S U B M A R I N E
```

ODD EVENS AND EVEN ODDS

1. 13; all the others are even numbers.
2. 16; all the others are multiples of 3.
3. 39; all the others are multiples of 7.
4. 91; all the others, when their separate digits are added together, make 6 (eg. 3 + 3 = 6; 4 + 2 = 6).
5. 71; all the others, when their separate digits are added together make 12.
6. 45; all the others are multiples of 8.
7. 42; all the others are odd numbers.
8. 87; all the others are multiples of 5.
9. 1511; all the others, when their separate digits are added together, make 7.
10. 156; all the others are multiples of 5.

NUMBING NUMBERS

1. 24; each number is 4 more than the previous number $(20 + 4 = 24)$

2. 7. Hands up all those who thought there was a catch to this one!

3. 2; each number is half the previous number.

4. 39; each number is the product of the two numbers which immediately precede it $(15 + 24 = 39)$.

5. 77; each number is the next multiple of 11.

6. 5; each number is 3 less than the previous number $(8 - 3 = 5)$.

7. 74; to get the second number add 2 to the first; to get the third add 4 to the second, and then 8, 16, etc. $(42 + 32 = 74)$.

8. 14; the numbers are all *descending* multiples of 7.

9. 46; to get the second number add 3 to the first and then each multiple of 3 (6, 9, etc.) $(34 + 12 = 46)$.

10. 43, 046, 721! Each number is the square of the previous number, ie. is obtained by multiplying the previous number by itself $(6561 \times 6561 = 43, 046, 721)$.

11. 19; the second number is 5 less than the first; the third is 4 less than the second; and so on $(20 - 1 = 19)$.

12. 27; simply add 4 to the previous number $(23 + 4 = 27)$.

13. 81; each number is the product of the two numbers immediately preceding it $(31 + 50 = 81)$.

14. 509; each number is 32 less the previous number $(541 - 32 = 509)$.

15. 29; each number is obtained by adding 3, 4, 5, etc. to the previous number $(22 + 7 = 29)$.

16. 4; each number is obtained by subtracting 5, 4, 3, etc. from the previous number (6 – 2 = 4).
17. 360; each number is obtained by multiplying the previous number by 2, 3, 4, etc. (72 × 5 = 360).
18. 223; each number is double the previous number plus 1 (111 × 2 = 222; 222 + 1 = 223).
19. 45; each number is a multiple of 9.
20. 39; each number, apart from the first one, is a multiple of 8 *minus* 1 (8 × 5 = 40; 40 – 1 = 39).

DOTTY DIGITS
1.
13 + 16 = 29
22 ÷ 2 = 11
13 + 49 + 3 = 65
39 − 18 = 21
8 × 16 = 128
2 × 30 = 60
49 + 67 = 116
12 ÷ 3 = 4

2	0	7	8	3	8	0	0	0	0
2	1	0	7	7	7	1	2	8	1
2	8	2	1	1	6	6	7	6	0
5	5	5	7	9	0	2	2	4	0
2	2	2	8	8	6	5	7	7	7
5	6	6	5	6	2	9	8	9	9
6	6	9	8	0	1	2	8	7	3
3	3	1	2	7	5	5	6	6	6
3	5	6	7	8	6	5	7	3	2
1	1	8	7	8	8	8	8	1	1

2.
60 × 22 = 1320
25 − 16 = 9
608 ÷ 4 = 152
33 + 671 = 704
1444 − 16 = 1428
13 × 2 = 26
144 ÷ 12 = 12
22 + 1 = 23

0	0	2	3	7	8	0	1	0	2
1	3	2	0	3	3	1	4	2	8
1	2	2	2	2	2	3	7	1	5
2	6	2	2	2	2	2	3	2	2
1	6	8	7	8	9	0	6	7	8
2	2	3	4	4	4	4	4	4	3
7	0	7	7	0	8	7	0	4	7
1	5	2	2	5	4	5	5	5	5
1	3	3	2	3	2	2	1	0	1
9	1	1	1	1	1	4	4	4	4

LOONY LOGIC

1. Gary – Kim Wilde; John – Beethoven; Fiona –
   Rick Astley; Lee – Madonna; Alison – Bananarama; Nick – The Pet Shop Boys.

2. 1. The United Kingdom; 2. East Germany; 3.
   France; 4. New Zealand; 5. Austria; 6. Norway;
   7. Switzerland; 8. Brazil.

3. Tracey – Australia; Johnathan – Spain; Helen –
   Iceland; Denise – Blackpool; Stuart – Greece;
   Elaine – The USA.

4. Tony – Synthesizer; Diane – Piano; Jackie –
   Oboe; Sean – Guitar; Nikki – Violin.

5. First – Martin – discus; Second – Simon – swimming; Third – Laura – javelin; Fourth – Jane –
   100 metres; Fifth – Mary – gymnastics.